Adventures From Lancashire

Edited By Kat Cockrill

First published in Great Britain in 2019 by:

 Young**Writers**® Est. 1991

Young Writers
Remus House
Coltsfoot Drive
Peterborough
PE2 9BF
Telephone: 01733 890066
Website: www.youngwriters.co.uk

Foreword

Dear Reader,

You will never guess what I did today! Shall I tell you?
Some primary school pupils wrote some diary entries
and I got to read them, and they were **excellent!**

They wrote them in school and sent them to us here at Young
Writers. We'd given their teachers some bright and funky
worksheets to fill in, and some fun and fabulous (and free)
resources to help spark ideas and get inspiration flowing.

And it clearly worked because **WOW!!** I can't believe
the adventures I've been reading about. Real people,
make believe people, dogs and unicorns, even objects like
pencils all feature and these diaries all have one thing in
common – they are **jam-packed** with imagination!

We live and breathe creativity here at Young Writers – it
gives us life! We want to pass our love of the written word
onto the next generation and what better way to do that
than to celebrate their writing by publishing it in a book!

It sets their work free from homework books and
notepads and puts it where it deserves to be – **out in
the world!** Each awesome author in this book should
be **super proud** of themselves, and now they've got proof
of their imagination, their ideas and their creativity in
black and white, to look back on in years to come!

Now that I've read all these diaries, I've somehow got to
pick some winners! Oh my gosh it's going to be difficult to
choose, but I'm going to have **so much fun** doing it!

Bye!

Kat

Contents

Imam Muhammad Zakariya School, Preston

Khadijah Desai (6)	55

Kingsfold Primary School, Penwortham

Marissa Knight (6)	56
Reece Vose (6)	57
Roel Lela (6)	58
Malachi Munetsi (6)	59
Mason Louis Hopwell (6)	60

Moss Side Primary School, Leyland

Declan Wilson (6)	61
Rosie Marie Kendall-Treadwell (6)	62
Amber Clews-Ashworth (6)	63
Lenny Burke (7)	64
Rosie Hadley (6)	65
Thomas Cafferky (6)	66
Sadie Wood (6)	67
Dominykas Alsauskas (6)	68
Rylea Johnson (6)	69
Boden Grimshaw (6)	70
Charlotte Grace Tierney (6)	71
Christie Allard (7)	72
Isaac Lucas (6)	73
Noah Gornall (6)	74
Taylor Hurst (7)	75
Harriet Jacqueline Lamb (6)	76
Hayden Thompson (6)	77
Noah Sherlock (6)	78
Jack Cooper (6)	79
Luke James Sucliff (6)	80

Oldham Hulme Grammar School, Oldham

Emily Samuels (6)	81
Mikaeel Iqbal (6)	82
Mika'il Amar Rafiq (7)	84
Vidhi Velji (7)	86
Thomas Ashurst (6)	87
Arissa Judge (7)	88
Georgia Kilpatrick (6)	89
Ammar Hussain (6)	90
Alessandro Guarino (6)	91
Poppy Victoria Sykes (6)	92

Rawdhatul Uloom Primary School, Burnley

Khadijah Tulkubra Khan (6)	93

Ribbleton Avenue Infant School, Preston

Salisha Vaghela (6)	94

St Anne's Catholic Primary School, Leyland

Caleb Flood (7)	95
Alice Ciara Myerscough (7)	96
Amelia Cartmell (7)	98
Abigail Cleece (7)	99

St Anne's Primary School, Denton

Willow Lea Layton (6)	100
Ruby Redfern (6)	101
Phoebe Alice Barnes (6)	102
Olivia Rainey (6)	103
Kobe Kayes (6)	104
Isabelle Louise Connor (6)	105
Lilah Mae Barratt (6)	106
Charlotte Delaney (6)	107
Freddie Millington (5)	108
Georgia Ward (6)	109
Abbie Carney (6)	110

Ethan Healey (6)	111	Matilde Pinto (6)	146
Lacey-Rae Cassidy (6)	112	Scarlett Faulkner (6)	147
Chloe McFarland (6)	113	Anthony White (6)	148
Ella Macfarlane (6)	114	Mollie Griffin (5)	149
Chloe Lewis (6)	115	Poppy Grace Atkinson (6)	150
Max Thewlis (6)	116	Andrei Toma Lupu (6)	151
Isabelle Chambers (6)	117	Joseph Green (6)	152
Darcie Royle (6)	118	Emma Gunn-Russell (6)	153
Dominic Cocca (6)	119	Harry Kirby (6)	154
Freya Rose Marland (6)	120	Darcie Savannah Collins (5)	155
Lexie Cooper (5)	121	Evan Millward (6)	156
		Giuseppe Ferlito (6)	157

St Gabriel's CE Primary School, Middleton

Weeton Primary School, Weeton

Jessica Rose Gibson (6)	122	Edward Hill (6)	158
Joshua Kian Swatkins (6)	123	Poppy Reid (6)	159
Carolina Mazur (6)	124	Poppie Mai Malone (6)	160
Aleeyah Jade Susan Samuels (6)	125	Phoebe Greener (5)	161
Ruby Lee Gibson (6)	126	Elliot Jack Bostock (6)	162
Grace Turner (5)	127	Bai Ebrahim Saine (6)	163
Towasin Jimoh (6)	128	Ebony Murphy (6)	164
Aroush Asaf (6)	129	Keevagh Quaggan (6)	165
Amelia-Jaye Josephine Jones-Horton (6)	130	Tommy James Edkins (6)	166
Zac H (6)	131		

Westwood Prep School, Oldham

Harry Carl Turner (6)	132
Jacob Harvey-Tait (6)	133
Elouise Blore (6)	134
Millie Brooke Humphries (6)	135
Lily-Rose Davies (6)	136
Isaac Harvey-Tait (6)	137
Noah-Kie Hudson (6)	138
Kenley Smith (5)	139

Safwan Noor Chowdhury (6)	167
Muhammed Saleem (6)	168

The Deans Primary School, Swinton

Lucas James Burgess (6)	140
Mia King (6)	141
Khadija Senussi (6)	142
Isabella Ho (6)	143
Alivia Wheeldon (6)	144
Jaxon Ronnie Openshaw (6)	145

The
Diaries

Dear Diary

I went to my dad's on Friday. We had a fun, great night. We roasted marshmallows and we had some popcorn, then we watched a movie. I slept with Max and Elly, the dogs, and they were licking me. In the morning, I had to go dancing. After dancing, we walked five and a half miles. I was very tired but, when I got home, I had some tea. The next day, my grandad and grandma came down. We went fishing but we didn't catch any fish. We also had a picnic and we got an ice cream, it was tasty. My brother had one as well, he said it was tasty and yummy! I liked it as well and I went out for tea on Sunday. I had some noodles and prawn crackers and a Fanta. It was tasty and beautiful.

Robyn Scarratt (7)
Audenshaw Primary School, Audenshaw

Dear Diary

Yesterday was a fabulous day for me and then it was bedtime, soon the clock struck midnight and a circle appeared in the wall! I jumped through and it went purple. When I opened my eyes, I was in a totally different world. It was Dinosaur-Dinosaur Land. The trees were a lovely shade of green and there were dinosaurs everywhere. The skies were blue but the clouds were green and the dinosaurs could talk! Soon, I found a little T-rex but its mother wasn't cute. Then, I spotted a big herd of brachiosaurus walking away from me. "Wait!" I yelled at them.

"What did you say?" a brachiosaurus answered.

I said, "Wait!"

"Why?" answered the brachiosaurus.

"Because I want to make friends with you!"
"Okay!"
Then, I said, "But, I have to go home now. I have time for a bubble gas ice cream!" I said. It tasted like a chocolate mousse and juice. Then I went back through the circle and back into my bedroom and fell asleep. It was such a good adventure!

Scarlett Rose McGuire (7)

Audenshaw Primary School, Audenshaw

Dear Diary

Today was so much fun and I went to a cool theme park called Magic Kingdom with my lovely family. I met the amazing Donald Duck, he is my favourite character and I bought a Donald Duck hat. We ate yummy snacks and I liked the delicious ice cream. I went on the exciting roller coasters and the big log flume, but I got super-wet. The weather in Florida is very warm, so I put suncream on and I had a good suntan. I drank a yummy blue slush and I met my amazing friends, Katie and Daniel. It was so much fun! Then, we also went out for dinner. I had a giant cheeseburger with curly fries and for dessert, I had a tasty waffle with yummy chocolate ice cream on top.

Matthew Clinton (7)
Audenshaw Primary School, Audenshaw

Dear Diary

You will not believe what happened today! I was having a picnic on a nice, green and grassy field when, suddenly, an orange, glittery and slimy alien came. It said its name was Gloopey and it would take me on an adventure to a planet called Slimy. It was covered in slimy rocks. We played hide-and-seek, it was so so fun, then I taught Gloopey how to play rock, paper, scissors. Gloopey really liked it. I started to miss Mum, Dad and my brother, so Gloopey took me home. Gloopey said he would keep visiting. Today was the best day ever because I made a friend who is out of this world!

Daisy Varrechia (7)
Audenshaw Primary School, Audenshaw

Dear Diary

Today, I went to a unicorn and mermaid castle. It was amazing, it had a balcony and ten maids. I got a chocolate cake, yummy! I had a nice, clean bathroom with lots of toys. It had a great school, it had a library with soft pillows. I liked the food, they had amazing food! I had a great teacher called Miss Kind and she always made it a lovely day. After lunch, we had a lovely afternoon. When I got home, I played with my friend. We played babies and dolls and played outside on the trampoline and the hula hoops. Then we had dinner and I went to bed.

Amelia Roberts (7)
Audenshaw Primary School, Audenshaw

Dear Diary

It finally came, my best moment of all! I went to the zoo with my family! My dream came true. First thing I saw, a tiger playing football. I went in to do the best, magical football skills I could do. Second thing I saw was a lion racing but it couldn't do it, the cheetah won, obviously! Third thing I did, I was just finishing my lunch and I saw a lion with its sly face looking at my lunch. I think it wanted to eat it. It ended being the best day ever and I will never forget it because it was fabulous!

Kobe Francis (7)
Audenshaw Primary School, Audenshaw

Dear Diary

Yesterday, I had a brilliant barbecue. There was cheese, sausages, crisps and me and my family played football and I scored the most! But, the food was delicious. Me and Robert also played games. After the barbecue, I watched the Megaladon, the shark was scary.

Today, I went on a frog hunt and I saw colourful frogs, like the Manchester bees. They were all over Stockport and we got tired legs. But, the sun was very hot, so we stopped to have a rest and a cold cola.

Henry Parker (7)
Audenshaw Primary School, Audenshaw

Dear Diary

After school, I went to the park with my best friend, Lilly. My favourite part was when I went on the swing because I went high in the sky and the sky was sparkling with white, puffy clouds. Then, it turned into dinner time and I had a corn and chicken butty. After, I went on a red, fast, slippy slide and I landed on my bottom. Then, I stopped to stroke a soft, fluffy dog. Next, I went into the sandpit. The sand was soft and deep. Then it was time to go home!

Lucy May Walton (7)
Audenshaw Primary School, Audenshaw

Dear Diary

The other day, I went to Mars with a talking cupcake and we did some gymnastics. Then we had a horse-riding party and invited a dragon, a unicorn and a mermaid. We had fun until the dragon spotted a secret, underground tunnel but, luckily, we found potions, slime and milkshakes, then we had a picnic and that was the end of the day.

Grace Young (7)
Audenshaw Primary School, Audenshaw

Dear Diary

Today, I went to the zoo! I saw a lion and then I ate lunch. We had pizza from the shop then, after I ate the pizza, I played with my slime. Then we went home and had a barbecue and we had a surprise in the garden, it was a swimming pool! I loved the swimming pool. I got in it, that was good. I also saw an elephant at the zoo!

Isla Lilly Carney (7)

Audenshaw Primary School, Audenshaw

Dear Diary

Yesterday, when I went to the summer fair, I saw Kobe and Oliver outside and Kobe and Oliver went to the bouncy castle so I went into it as well. We had fun together and Oliver let me get a five duck (he was cheating by holding the duck) and I got two sweets. Then we had to go home, except for Kobe and Oliver.

Kevin Kone (7)
Audenshaw Primary School, Audenshaw

Dear Diary

It has been quite strange recently. The other day, I heard strange noises coming from the end of the bed. I heard a weird, gurgling noise. I was wide awake for two hours but it was Sunday night and Monday the next day so I didn't hear the gurgling for a while. I said to myself, "I'm sure it will stop soon!" It didn't though. I decided to look under the bed and I saw a five-eyed creature with four arms and a tiny pet six-legged dog. It gurgled as I patted the six-legged dog. The creature clambered out from under the bed. It began to float out the open window. I shouted, "Wait!" As he turned to me, he blinked his eyes individually. He gurgled as he made me float. We floated all the way to Mars. When we arrived, there were a bunch of creatures having a picnic, so I joined in for a while and then went home and went back to bed.

Devon Curtis (7)

Avondale Primary School, Darwen

Dear Diary

Yesterday, I got sucked into a video game! The video game was called Rainbow Land. I met a unicorn, but then I saw my friend, Erin. She said, "Hi!" I also said hi. Rainbow Land was really nice. The floor was cotton candy. Me and Erin ate the cotton candy, then walked onto a rainbow. The rainbow was made out of rainbow laces! Then we went to sleep.

In the morning, we thought it was a dream but, when we looked at the floor, it was not a dream. We went for a walk. We saw a branch and sat on it. Erin fell asleep on me again. I fell asleep as well. When we woke up, we weren't in the video game. It was a boring day. But, when I went to sleep again, I was in it again! I went to find Erin, I found her lying on the floor. Then, I saw a girl. I walked up and said, "Hi." She said hi as well. I said that my name was Ruby.

She said, "I'm Livy!"
I said, "Can we be friends?"
Livy said, "Yes!" We all became friends and
went to Livy's tree house.

Ruby Grace Dickinson (7)
Avondale Primary School, Darwen

Dear Diary

A few weeks ago, after school, I went to Ruby's house and then to Olivia's house. We went to the forest and climbed up this tree. A few hours later, I got up and explored. I saw a strange door, it was on a branch. Olivia walked into it. It was funny. I knocked on the strange, little door and a weird little girl came out. "Hello! I'm Pop's Pop. I made some cola. Want some?"
"Oh, thank you!" I said. "We would love some! Oh no, I nearly forgot, is there anything for us to do up here?" I said.
The strange little girl said, "Yes, at the top of the tree, there is a little land!" said Pop's Pop.
I said thank you and we went all the way up. I climbed the ladder, the others followed me. At the top, we saw loads and loads of toys. I saw a sign, it said, *Take what you want!* But, then, an alarm went off. We got trapped in!

I started to panic. Then, I ate and drank a potion and went back home.

Erin Jennifer Taylor (7)

Avondale Primary School, Darwen

Dear Diary

Yesterday, I was playing with my Lego and something happened to me. I went into my Lego and I turned into a Lego person and I looked around and I was in Legoland. Then, a big, giant Lego dragon came but then I heard a slinging and springing noise! It was Spider-Man! Then, we defeated the dragon together. But, then, I heard a dinosaur and everyone in the city screamed and he breathed fire! We jumped on him and he went to the ground. Then we drank smoothies but, after that, a tiger came and got Spider-Man. Then I tipped my smoothie over him and he went away, crying. I told the tiger, "If you want, you can live with me but only if you stop destroying things and let Spider-Man go!"

Elliot Wheeler (7)
Avondale Primary School, Darwen

Dear Diary

Yesterday, I went on my go-kart with my brother called Lucas. Lucas played on it too, it was really fun. But, then, me and Lucas went back inside for a drink, then me and Lucas went outside. Then we saw a monster! It was friendly and fluffy so me and Lucas let the fluffy monster ride my go-kart! Then, we saw a superhero who went on my go-kart and the superhero went to the park. Me, Lucas and the monster followed him to the park and I put the monster on the slide and the superhero went on the swing with Lucas. Then we played on my go-kart. Then we had a snack while we played on my pink and purple beautiful go-kart!

Leila Harrison (7)
Avondale Primary School, Darwen

Dear Diary

Last week, on Thursday, I went to my aunty's horse stable, it was very smelly. I went into Marty's stable, Marty's the horse by the way. My aunty said, "Why don't you have a ride on the horse?"
I said, "Yes, that would be great!" So, I gave Marty her saddle and some water. I hopped on her and off I went with my mum and my aunty. First, we rode to the park. We had a picnic, the horse pinched my sandwich! Finally, we dropped the horses off. My mum and I went back to the stables. Marty suddenly gave us a fright. She turned into a unicorn! I wondered what would happen next.

Poppy Olivia Mcdermott (7)
Avondale Primary School, Darwen

Dear Diary

Last Friday, I explored the funfair. It took fifty-one hours and I brought Elsie, Mum, Dad and Bryn. We can't forget Reuben! When we got there, me and Elsie met a unicorn, a beautiful mermaid queen and a fairy. Reuben is obsessed with Pokémon and there was a real-life Pokémon! He also told me he had the Pokémon on a card! After that, my family, and me of course, went into a secret tunnel. We all made wonderful sweets, brilliant bars of chocolate, some slime and a milkshake. They were so delicious (except the slime!) Finally, we set off home. It was sad but at least we had fun!

Gracie Leigh Williams (7)
Avondale Primary School, Darwen

Dear Diary

On Sunday, I went with my friends, Molly and Katie, to the abandoned shop. We climbed through a broken window and searched through the room and up the creepy stairs. Then, we found a button so we all pressed it together. It revealed a secret tunnel and I led them through. We saw a unicorn and a fairy! They had a chocolate and strawberry milkshake and slime. The fairy loved the slime, it was purple and glittery, just like her. Just after lunch, me, Molly and Katie went horse-riding. Well, unicorn-riding of course because we were riding a unicorn! Meanwhile, the fairy was camouflaging the button again!

Isabelle Jones (7)
Avondale Primary School, Darwen

Dear Diary

A few weeks ago, I went to the funfair with a monster and a friend, Jack. I got three chocolate milkshakes. We went on a slide and it was big but blue. Me, Jack and the monster found a secret hole and, in it, there was the monster's family! He was green and fluffy and I hugged the monster. The milkshake had made the monster sleepy, so he went to sleep. We found a way out. We played on all the rides. We had a good time and we had a chat. We had a wander around and played football and hide-and-seek. We had burgers and chips for lunch. After that, at 7pm, we went home.

Rylan Turner-Cathie (7)
Avondale Primary School, Darwen

Dear Diary

On Sunday, I am having a birthday party. I am inviting Charley and Jacoby, we are going to play party games. We are going to play pass-the-parcel and more party games. When we are done, we are going to have a Toy Story birthday cake. But then Charley and Jacoby will have to leave.

On Tuesday, it will be my real birthday with Charley and Jacoby. I will be seven. We are going to the cinema in Blackburn. We are going to have popcorn, a drink and sweets. We will watch Toy Story 4. The main characters are Woody, Buzz, Forky, Bunny, Ducky and Bonnie!

Samuel Beswick (6)
Avondale Primary School, Darwen

Dear Diary

The other day, I went on a rocket to space and I saw an alien from space and we had a picnic. Then, we saw a superhero and there was a dinosaur who was very mean and he ate all our picnic! So, we threw slime at him and he was all messy and he turned nice. Then, we had some sweets and we saw a Pokémon ball so we picked it up. We had lots of Pokémon cards and we looked at all the Pokémon. Later on, we got chips, it was amazing and then we had to go home. It was the best day!

Leon Smillie (7)
Avondale Primary School, Darwen

Dear Diary

I have a scrape on my head because I did something silly like fall on the bumpy floor. I also went to a gymnasium with my friend, Poppy. We did frontflips and fab cartwheels. Me and Poppy practised our cartwheels, frontflips, backflips and side flips at the beach. We had decided to go to Italy because we loved Italy so we went to the Italian beach to practise our fab cartwheels, frontflips, backflips and side flips. When we went home, we went to bed.

Ella Arnold (7)
Avondale Primary School, Darwen

Dear Diary

A few weeks ago, I went to a bouncy funfair with my friend called George. When we got there, we saw some yummy ice cream, beautiful slides, amazing magic tricks, quick carousels and super trampolines! We almost went on every single ride and we both had £2000.19 each. But, our favourite part was the Pokémon water slide. It wasn't a real water slide, it was inflatable!

James Holden (6)
Avondale Primary School, Darwen

Dear Diary

The other day, I was in the woods, walking and I saw a unicorn with a baby unicorn. The mummy unicorn and the baby unicorn let me stroke them. But, then, a fairy turned them into a galaxy and then there was a war. They had the power to turn into galaxies so all of the unicorns and people needed to save the world. They said, "Come on!" We all went to save the world!

Eleanor Rawlinson (7)
Avondale Primary School, Darwen

Dear Diary

One month ago, I went to the fire station with my mum. In the fire station was a gym, they were old so they needed to get fit. When I grow up, I want to be a fireman. In the fire station, I went on the fire van. I made cupcakes and the icing was a fire logo. My mum went to the gym to exercise because she wanted to get fit.

Isaac Ivor Hopson (7)
Avondale Primary School, Darwen

Dear Diary

The other day, I got a superhero costume and George got one too. Then a villain came and tied us up! We broke the rope and then we found an abandoned house. We went in. There were lots of zombies and then we killed all of them. We went to go, then a zombie grabbed my foot, so I sliced its hand off!

Xander Layne Doran-Martin (7)
Avondale Primary School, Darwen

Dear Diary

On Sunday, I went to space on a red rocket with my best friend Rylan and we stayed for three days. We brought four chocolate bars. We also went swimming and met some aliens. We had a picnic and had four chocolate bars to share and some milkshakes.

Jack Matthew Clough (7)
Avondale Primary School, Darwen

Dear Diary

The other day, I went to the beach with a monster. At 2pm, we got there in a car. I played with the monster and we went on the slide. Then we had dinner and a banana and toffee yoghurt!

Jamie Naylor (7)

Avondale Primary School, Darwen

Dear Diary

Yesterday, I went to the zoo. I went on the bus with my friends. The elephants were hiding in their house so I went to see the monkeys and the rhinos. I had my dinner with the giraffes. I liked the lions and the cheetahs best. I had a wonderful day!

Isabelle Yates (4)

Bickershaw CE Primary School, Bickershaw

Dear Diary

Yesterday, I went to the zoo. I went to see the rhinos and the elephants were hiding in their home. We had a picnic with the giraffes and buffalos. Next, I went to the bat cave and it was stinky. The bat flew into my hand. I had a fantastic day!

Thomas Fisher (5)

Bickershaw CE Primary School, Bickershaw

Dear Diary

Yesterday, I went to the zoo. The jaguar was licking his paws. The sun bear was climbing on a tree. It was a great day.

Ellis Joseph Reeve (4)

Bickershaw CE Primary School, Bickershaw

Dear Diary

Today, I went to Blackpool zoo with my friend Hatti. We saw a cage, it was massive! After that, we heard a growl. It was a tiger! There were lions, zebra, monkeys, flamingoes, wolves and otters. Then, we had a picnic. It had all sorts of things like sandwiches, tomatoes and chives.
After that, because we didn't have enough food, we decided to look for a shop. We found a chest, it was silver and really shiny. Then, a little fairy popped out of it wearing a gold, sparkly dress with tiny yellow flowers on it. The fairy said, "If you find a jewel, bring it to this chest, otherwise you won't be able to fly!"
So, then, the next day, we went to Thompson Park and found nine jewels. We only had to get one more. Then we went to the cinema and found two. So, we just threw one away and kept the other one.

After that, we quickly drove to Blackpool zoo, then we locked them safely in their place for the fairy. The fairy sent us a thank you letter and we thanked her!

Ami Derbyshire (7)

Crawshawbooth Primary School, Crawshawbooth

Dear Diary

Today, I went to the beach with my friends Ami and Hatti. We played on the sand and we saw a sad sea turtle. On its leg, there was some plastic. We all went over to the turtle and removed the plastic. I looked up to the sea and said, "Look at that sea!" Ami and Hatti looked up at the sea and glared at each other. They thought of an idea. We quickly got changed into our swimming costumes and went into the sea. Before we went into the sea, we grabbed a net. We started scooping out litter from the sea and put it in a bucket. After we were done, we put the plastic in the plastic recycling bin and we carried on playing.

Natasha Hargreaves (7)
Crawshawbooth Primary School, Crawshawbooth

Dear Diary

Today, I went to Manchester City's stadium for a tour. My mum and dad took me because we love Man City. I was really excited and happy I was going there. When we arrived, our tour guide took us inside. The dressing room was fantastic, the players had their pictures on the wall and their names! I saw the pitch with the big, brilliant City badge on it. I sat in Pep's super seat, pretending to be him. I hope I can watch the players play a match next time. Sergio Agüero is the best, he always makes sneaky runs behind the other team! The day was brilliant!

Asa Tinker (7)
Crawshawbooth Primary School, Crawshawbooth

Dear Diary

The other day, we went to the park and we went to the sand park. I got a big ice cream with all different ingredients on. Next, I did some gardening and I helped my dad wash the car. We got wet, it was fun!

Izabelle Smith (7)

Crawshawbooth Primary School, Crawshawbooth

Dear Diary

Yesterday, me and my friend Joseph were playing Jurassic Park. I accidentally dropped my controller in my drink and it sucked us into the game on the last level. We had to chase the Endo-rex on a helicopter. Some pterodactyls dropped. Joseph jumped on the alpha pterodactyl. Joseph got all of the pterodactyls out of the way. I shot the Endo-rex with a net but it broke the net. Then we saw Patrick and George, they made a trap with a giant cage and some meat. The Endo-rex took the meat, then the cage dropped. We found a portal. It was nearly dinner time. We went into the portal, then my mum called us for dinner!

Cillian Hayes (7)
Guardian Angels RC Primary School, Elton

Dear Diary

Yesterday, I went for a ride on my pony with my best friend. My pony is called Indigo. We ended up in a magical land. Indigo turned rainbow-coloured and was shimmering with sparkles. The land was grey with no colour. We saw a riddle and it said: *You need to find the rainbow fairies to get the colour back!* There were two fairies and two lands. The first land was Snowball Falls. The second land was Summer Fire Canyon. We arrived at Snowball Falls and asked the fairy, Snow, if we could have the crystal. She said yes. We had a picnic after we went to Summer Fire Canyon. It was delicious.

Courtney Khan (7)
Guardian Angels RC Primary School, Elton

Dear Diary

Last week, me and my cousin Jasmine saw a superhero and she was going to space! We followed her on our pearlescent rocket ship. Not long after, the superhero spotted us and Jasmine was nervous because we had never seen a superhero before. We landed on a green and purple planet. On the planet, we found lots of aliens with ten eyes. They told us that the alien war was going to slime Earth. Me, Jasmine and the superhero rushed to stop them as fast as we could! They were not going to slime the world! Then we had a big party and everyone was invited. We even had a cinema, it was the best day ever!

Ava Rose Le Blanc (7)
Guardian Angels RC Primary School, Elton

Dear Diary

On Sunday, I went to space. I landed on the moon. When I saw Jupiter, it was magnificent and it had this red spot which was round. It had a thunderstorm too. I stayed for twelve hours. Before I had my lunch, I did gymnastics. I was floating around the moon. Then I had my lunch. I had a chocolate milkshake and a sandwich. Then I saw a green, slimy alien. It was chatting to me and I did not like it. I had one minute left, so I went home but he followed me. Then I locked it out of my door and got ready for bed. I was sleepy. The window was open and the moon was shining bright.

Hannah Moore (7)
Guardian Angels RC Primary School, Elton

Dear Diary

Last week, I went to Legoland with my mum, dad and my friend, Joseph. We had fun. After we came in an amazing, magnificent entrance, we went on some rides and, one of them, you had to shoot zombies with cannons. Then, we had lunch. I had a hot dog with Sprite and Joseph had the same. Then we went to the play part and I played on the climbing wall and I challenged Joseph and he won. We slid down the slide and we went on a Ninjago plane. Then we went to the gift shop. I bought a Star Trek Lego and Joseph bought an electronic supercar and it was light blue and orange.

George Whalley (7)
Guardian Angels RC Primary School, Elton

Dear Diary

Last week, I went to the funfair with my best friend, Celia. We went on the magnificent waltzers, then we got on the ghost train, it was pretty scary. Then we went on the swinging chairs, they were pretty high! They went so high that they made me feel sick. Next, we went on the merry-go-round. We went two times around, it was pretty calm. Then we went to a cafe. I had a burger and Celia had a hot dog. I had a chocolate milkshake too! Celia had the same. We liked it so much that we took three for the way home on the tram!

Amelie Johnson-Kitchen (7)
Guardian Angels RC Primary School, Elton

Dear Diary

Last week, me and my friend Amelia went to the huge funfair. When we got there, we went on the big, rainbow Ferris wheel and I sat on the pink chair. I was so so excited for the show. Inside, there was a huge, huge elephant and he juggled with ten balls. I was very shocked. He even did it on his back! We went out of the show and went on the swings. I went super-fast and high. Then there was a horse but they weren't real so I didn't go on it. My friend Amelia did go on it. Then we went home.

Scarlett Collins (7)
Guardian Angels RC Primary School, Elton

Dear Diary

On Sunday, me and my best friend Sam and Mum went to the park. We played in the sandpit, then we went down the slippery slide. A few minutes later, we went on the climbing frame. Later, we went to the fast, green roundabout, then we played football! After that, we went to the zipline. When we got to it, we heard a loud sound. It sounded like metal so I grabbed my pickaxe and mined and fell into a tunnel. So, Sam jumped in and we explored the tunnel and found the secret base of a villain!

Montgomery Nelson (7)
Guardian Angels RC Primary School, Elton

Dear Diary

During the summer holidays, I went to the fairy woods. I was so excited. When I was there, I saw a precious unicorn and a sparkly, beautiful, colourful fairy! They were real and I followed them quietly. Then I saw a little cottage. Then something grabbed me and it was an elf. It said, "Let's try together to ask if we could stay at their little cottage!"
"Of course!" said the fairy. "Get a hot chocolate, find a big, pink bed, make yourself at home!"

Tabitha Crowther (6)
Guardian Angels RC Primary School, Elton

Dear Diary

At midnight, on Sunday, a twelve-eyed alien crashed through my window but I knew it was only my friend, Ava. She'd been turned into an alien! We were friends. Then, I made a rocket and went to the moon. On the moon, there were a lot of Pokémon in the sky. A spaceship abducted my rocket and I couldn't get home. A silly dragon tried to help me and he fell off the moon. Would I get home? I made dragon skin slime. Finally, I got off the moon and back home!

Freya Barnes (8)
Guardian Angels RC Primary School, Elton

Dear Diary

Last week, I went to the huge trampoline park with my mum, dad and my little brother. When I got there, I bought some trampoline socks. When we got to the trampolines, I jumped really, really high. Then it was lunchtime. We had a picnic. My little brother, Charlie, was scared because he didn't want to jump on the trampolines. Then my brother jumped and he enjoyed it. After that, I went to the shop, went to the car and drove home.

Harrison Burgess (7)
Guardian Angels RC Primary School, Elton

Dear Diary

Yesterday, I went to the apartment. Three hours later, I walked to the spaceship. I was ready to go. Three... two... one... blast-off! I flew into space. I landed on the moon and got out of my spaceship. I saw a monster, it had ten eyes, it was crazy! It chased me around. it was so scary! I spotted the monster again, I was worried it would get me. I got back into the spaceship and I got back home.

Andrew Campbell Foster (7)

Guardian Angels RC Primary School, Elton

Dear Diary

Last year, I went to Training Area 1 and met Pikachu. Pikachu was battling Super Swirl. Pikachu was getting ready for the Electric Ball. Then, Super Swirl did Swirl Teleport and Electric Ball missed Super Swirl but, luckily, Electric Ball went through Super Swirl's teleport bubble and knocked her out. Pikachu won!

Joshua Schofield (7)
Guardian Angels RC Primary School, Elton

Dear Diary

Last week, I went to Pokémon Land. We got a ticket, it cost eleven pounds. There were a lot of Pokémon and it was crowded with people. I saw Pikachu meeting other people, then we went to the castle. It was magnificent!

Tasos Athanasiadis (7)
Guardian Angels RC Primary School, Elton

Dear Diary

On the weekend, me and my sister went to our friend's house. We made a scary monster and took a picture of it. We ate delicious pasties, then we played hide-and-seek. I always win because I'm very good at hiding. When my mum and dad picked me up, I had a surprise. My mum and dad had got us something, it was milkshake! Finally, we went home!

Khadijah Desai (6)
Imam Muhammad Zakariya School, Preston

Dear Diary

Yesterday, I was camping. Last night, I was asleep when, suddenly, I woke up! Outside the tent, there was a magical unicorn and, guess what it wanted to do? It wanted to play with me! The unicorn took me to a swimming pool and, suddenly, a mermaid popped up and I jumped out of my skin. Then my cute, pink, sparkly monster teddy came to life. It ran up to us and, in a cute voice, said, "I love you!"

My family woke up and said, "Where has Marissa gone? She went to the swimming pool!" They found me and all my family said, "I love you!" And then my magical things and I went back to the tent. Finally, I went home.

Marissa Knight (6)

Kingsfold Primary School, Penwortham

Dear Diary

This morning, I got dressed and a ninja knocked at my door. I opened my door and I let him in and we played Fortnite and Ark and Ninja said, "Should we play Minecraft, Forza 4 and Roblox?" Then, outside, I saw zombies. I saw a superhero and they killed the zombies. Then I saw a lion and I saw Pikachu. I saw dragons and tigers and secret tunnels and treasure and me and the ninja saw a wizard.
He said, "Shazam! You will get my powers!"

Reece Vose (6)
Kingsfold Primary School, Penwortham

Dear Diary

Last night, I woke up from bed, then I went downstairs but it was blocked. I didn't know what to do, it was blocked by an alien. Then my mum came downstairs. "Why is it blocked?" said Mum, "What did you do?"
"I didn't do anything!"
"Who did it?"
"It was the alien!"
"But, I can't seem him?"

Roel Lela (6)
Kingsfold Primary School, Penwortham

Dear Diary

The other day, a monster came on the TV then there was a flash. I ran away, it was creepy. It made a noise and did a call. The Incredible Cam came to the rescue, he was a superhero. I didn't know he'd come to help me and ran away because I was scared.

Malachi Munetsi (6)

Kingsfold Primary School, Penwortham

Dear Diary

Last night, I floated to the moon. When I got there, I saw some superheroes. I saw aliens, they got me and grabbed me and took me to jail. Iron Man helped me to get out of the spooky jail and then me and Iron Man flew away. Then, they got us in the cave!

Mason Louis Hopwell (6)
Kingsfold Primary School, Penwortham

Dear Diary

On Saturday, I went to the park and when I went to the park I went on the monkey bars and I went on the slide and I saw a Doberman. I went on the slide and then the swings and then I got an ice cream. After that, I went to the shop. I went with my mum and she let us have some sweets. I got sour Chewiits. They were really sour! Then we went home and went to bed and my dad was last.
On Sunday, I was happy, so were my mum and dad.
Yesterday, my dad was off work!

Declan Wilson (6)

Moss Side Primary School, Leyland

Dear Diary

Yesterday, I went to the funfair. I went with my friends and I went on the Ferris wheel while my friend got some candyfloss. Then I had some blue candyfloss. My friend said it was very yummy and so did I. We went to ride on a horse, it was very fun. My friend said that it was very fun too. I went to the park. After that, I went to the park and the slide. I said, "Woo hoo!" So did my friend. Then I went on the roundabout, it made me very, very dizzy!

Rosie Marie Kendall-Treadwell (6)
Moss Side Primary School, Leyland

Dear Diary

On Tuesday, I went to Beavers. I went with my family and friends. I saw a unicorn. We danced and we did gymnastics.

Yesterday, I went to the park. I went with my best friends. We went on the slide and we went on the monkey bars. Then we saw a mermaid!

On Sunday, I went to the funfair. I went with two superheroes. We went on a helter-skelter. Then we saw an ugly monster. Then, the two superheroes scared it away. I had a fantastic day!

Amber Clews-Ashworth (6)

Moss Side Primary School, Leyland

Dear Diary

On Saturday, I went to space. I saw an alien. It said, "Blubar!" Next, I went to the funfair. I played a game where there were six balls and I had to kick a ball into the hole. I got three points. Then William played some rugby. He won 5-2. Me and William played hook-a-duck. I gave my prize to William. He said, "Thank you!" It was a big raccoon teddy! He gave me some treasure, it was a red diamond.

Lenny Burke (7)
Moss Side Primary School, Leyland

Dear Diary

The other day, I went to the park with my family and we went on the swings and the slides. I went to the zoo and I saw a tiger and I went on Monday. I saw an elephant at the zoo and I had a picnic. We ate sandwiches and some fruit, which was an apple, and we went for a walk and all the animals escaped and stole all the food. When we came back, there was no food so we looked and looked but we couldn't find the food!

Rosie Hadley (6)
Moss Side Primary School, Leyland

Dear Diary

Yesterday, I flew into space and we landed on the moon. Then we found a secret tunnel. When we went inside, it was a dragon cave. Then we had lunch with the dragon and it blew fire but the superheroes stopped it. We ran away and we ran past the zoo, then we ran back to the zoo and went inside. We saw some zebra and some lions and some parrots. We had a lovely time.

Thomas Cafferky (6)
Moss Side Primary School, Leyland

Dear Diary

On Sunday, I went to the park. I went with my family and friends. At the park, I went on the slides. I climbed up a ladder and looked in the window. When I looked through the window, I didn't see my dad and mum. When I got down, I could see them. I had a picnic. I had an apple and a sandwich with cheese and tomatoes. I had a lovely time!

Sadie Wood (6)
Moss Side Primary School, Leyland

Dear Diary

On Wednesday, I went to the beach with my family. We collected some pretty shells and we made a sandcastle.
On Sunday, I saw a Pokémon. We ran around, it was fun. We had lunch with it and we played some games and he was called Pikachu! He was funny and, after that, we had dinner with him and that was great.

Dominykas Alsauskas (6)
Moss Side Primary School, Leyland

Dear Diary

The other day, I went to swimming with Lucas. We did torpedos going through hoops. Then I went to the park. I went on the big slide and I went on the roundabout. Then I went on the trampoline and the funfair. I played hook-a-duck, then I went on the bouncy castle. Then I went in a ball floating on water.

Rylea Johnson (6)
Moss Side Primary School, Leyland

Dear Diary

I went to Alton Towers in October because it was the Monster Fest. First, I went on the ghost train and I shot all of the ghosts. Then I went on a ride and it went so fast that I was feeling amazing. I went to play hide-and-seek and I hid behind the ghost train and I won and Keiran hid but I found him!

Boden Grimshaw (6)
Moss Side Primary School, Leyland

Dear Diary

Last week, I went to the beach with my family. We went in the sea and we saw a mermaid.

On Saturday, we went to the zoo. We saw giraffes, lions and tigers and penguins and gorillas. An orange gorilla wiped its poo on the window and it ate it. It was funny. Then we got slime to play with.

Charlotte Grace Tierney (6)
Moss Side Primary School, Leyland

Dear Diary

Yesterday, I went to the park with my family. I played games. I played catch and I went on the slide and I saw a unicorn. Then I went to the sweet shop to get some sweets and I saw a fairy in the air. I found a shark but the shark was lonely, so I had a party with the shark. I loved it!

Christie Allard (7)

Moss Side Primary School, Leyland

Dear Diary

Yesterday, I saw a wood burner in my back garden, then I brought some wood to go in the wood burner.
Then, on Saturday, I saw a dinosaur in the woods, then me and the dinosaur went fishing. Then there was something in the water. It was a Mosasaurus! We ran until we were home.

Isaac Lucas (6)
Moss Side Primary School, Leyland

Dear Diary

On Friday, I went to the zoo with my family. At the zoo, we saw a tiger and a butterfly. At the zoo, we also saw a koala and zebra and hippo. After all that, we went to the funfair. At the funfair, we went on a Ferris wheel and did hook-a-duck. I liked the zoo best.

Noah Gornall (6)
Moss Side Primary School, Leyland

Dear Diary

On Friday, I went to the park with my best friend and we saw a Pokémon. We played football with him and someone was on the swing. His chocolate fell out of his pocket and, then, the Pokémon ate his chocolate and it was all gone. I really enjoyed it.

Taylor Hurst (7)
Moss Side Primary School, Leyland

Dear Diary

Yesterday, I saw a path. I went down it and I found a secret tunnel. I went through it and I saw a fairy garden. I shrunk down. I made friends with the fairy princess. We had a picnic, it was amazing. I stayed in Fairy Land and I got to be a princess.

Harriet Jacqueline Lamb (6)

Moss Side Primary School, Leyland

Dear Diary

The other day, I went to the park and the zoo and, at the zoo, I saw a monkey and they also had a tarantula. At the park, I went on the slide and the swings and I jumped off the swings. I went on the monkey bars and on the roundabout and it was great!

Hayden Thompson (6)
Moss Side Primary School, Leyland

Dear Diary

I went to the funfair and I saw a Pokémon and I went with my family and got a smoothie. I got a milkshake. I also got slime. I played with it! It was so much fun. I also went on a roller coaster.

Noah Sherlock (6)
Moss Side Primary School, Leyland

Dear Diary

On Monday, I went to the park with my family. We went down the slide and then we had a party at the park with a dragon and we went on the swings with the dragon. I had a wonderful time!

Jack Cooper (6)
Moss Side Primary School, Leyland

Dear Diary

On Monday, I went to see Pokémon with my friends. At the end, we went to the funfair. We went on a roller coaster and we went on six times! It was really fun there!

Luke James Sucliff (6)
Moss Side Primary School, Leyland

Dear Diary

Yesterday was the most amazing day. We were on holiday in France. Because it was a beautiful, sunny day Uncle Pete and my two cousins asked if I would like to go snorkelling with them, I immediately said yes. Ethan went first but ran out straight away shouting, "The sea is freezing!" Rhys was a little braver and stayed in there for two minutes. Then it was my turn. First, Uncle Pete showed me how to breathe with the snorkel on. I was a little scared at first but, then, I found the courage to swim deeper under the sea. To my amazement, the snorkel magically stretched longer and longer, allowing me to dive deeper into the ocean. I saw lots of fish and made friends with a beautiful mermaid. She swam with me and we sang songs, then it was time for me to swim up to the surface.

Emily Samuels (6)
Oldham Hulme Grammar School, Oldham

Dear Diary

My parents asked me what I would like to do when I grow taller. I said, "I want to make cool movies and invent some amazing things and I want to be a doctor to help people!" Finally, I said, "I want to write stories that make people laugh and jump!" My mum asked, "How are you going to do all those things at once Mikaeel?"
So, I started thinking about how I could do all those fun things and I decided first to be a doctor to learn about people, then to write a story and make it into a movie. Lastly, I would invent something to help people.
I am so excited! My dad always says, "Shoot for the moon, even if you miss, you'll land among the stars!"
One day, I will have a house and dig a swimming pool in the garden and put a slide coming down from my bedroom. I will share my fun with my kids and everyone.

And I will be able to gobble up ice creams! Yummy!
Every night before I sleep, I will dream about it and I will one day look at the moon with a telescope and say, "Thank you!" when I achieve it!

Mikaeel Iqbal (6)
Oldham Hulme Grammar School, Oldham

Dear Diary

Today, me and my cousins went to the fair. We went on the biggest roller coaster ever! When we got on the ride, it was so fast it blew some people's hair off. When the roller coaster reached the water, it went up slowly and then it was flying extremely high and landed with a *bang!* The roller coaster was fine because it had metal wheels.

The next ride we went on was a water slide. It went up and down, up and down a few times. When we reached the ramp, we started flying really high, so high that we thought we were touching the sky. After flying really high, we laid back on the water slide which ended at the beach. At the end, we went to a secret tunnel. The mission was to find a cave by crossing through different hurdles. When we swang the ropes, we wore a helmet. When we climbed the wall, we wore a belt and when we went under the water, we swam to find a key to unlock the elevator.

When we reached the elevator, we pressed floor 99 where we found the hidden cave which was a toy shop. All of the toys were for free!

Mika'il Amar Rafiq (7)
Oldham Hulme Grammar School, Oldham

Dear Diary

My cousin and uncle have a dog called Lucky and he is a boy. Lucky is a white, fluffy, small and very cute puppy. Lucky is extremely playful and loves messing the carpet up. Lucky loves running around in the backyard and his hair blows back. Lucky sometimes eats grass and then feels sick. It's cute when Lucky sleeps sideways. Whenever he has a bath at the salon, he looks like a girl. Lucky eats his dog food but he can eat bananas, carrots, white rice and even chappati.

After his lunch, he likes to have a little nap. Lucky looks funny and cute when he sleeps. Lucky scratched his head with his feet. I would love to have a puppy because they are playful and can cheer you up. If I had a dog, I would call it Mia.

Vidhi Velji (7)
Oldham Hulme Grammar School, Oldham

Dear Diary

Today, I went to the Grand Prix. I went in the car and it took two hours to get there. When I got there, we went to watch the practice and then we went to watch the real race. I felt excited, the cars were really noisy. Red Bull crashed and went off the track and Lewis won. I went up to the podium and saw Lewis and he sprayed me with champagne. Lewis came over and asked if I wanted to do some driving in his car with him. I said, "Yes, yes, yes!"
When the practice started, I was driving the car and won against all the racers, even Vettel and Bottas. Then, it was race time and I was racing in the car and I won. I felt happy. I held the trophy up and sprayed champagne on Lewis Hamilton. Best day ever!

Thomas Ashurst (6)
Oldham Hulme Grammar School, Oldham

Dear Diary

Today was the worst day ever. When I woke up, it was night-time and I was the tooth fairy. I got so many calls and messages saying teeth had fallen out. The worst thing of all was that I had to make my own house made out of teeth. It was awful, I hated it. I made a wish, I said, "I wish I was back to normal..." But, my wish didn't come true. Also, I was tiny. I had tiny pink wings, two tiny blue eyes and I was so tired. Finally, I built my tooth house, then I went to sleep. When I woke up, guess what? I was back to normal. Never try to be like someone else because you might hate it. My family asked where I was so I had to tell them the whole story start to end. I gave everyone a big hug.

Arissa Judge (7)
Oldham Hulme Grammar School, Oldham

Dear Diary

I would like to tell you about my amazing adventure at the funfair. One sunny morning, I woke up very early, then my mummy woke up. She had some very exciting news and she told us we were going to the funfair. I was so excited so my mum said that my friend could come too! After we had breakfast, we set off.

After a while, we were there and I saw my other friend, Lily. Then we went on the Ferris wheel but, just then, the Ferris wheel stopped and we were right at the top and we were so frightened and started to scream for help but nobody could hear us. Then we realised the police could hear us and we got saved by a helicopter and we stopped worrying and had the best day ever!

Georgia Kilpatrick (6)

Oldham Hulme Grammar School, Oldham

Dear Diary

I am going to tell you about my trip to Spain. When I was at the airport, I checked in my luggage, then, after that, I boarded the plane. The airline was Ryanair. Then we took off. After the two hour flight, we landed at Barcelona airport. At the airport, we met my cousins. Their names are Raheel and Bisma. They said, "Hola!" to me which means 'hello' in Spanish. After that, we got in a taxi. The taxi drove us to their flat. The next day, we went to the park, then we went shopping. After that, we went to Plaça de Catalunya. We saw loads of pigeons and we fed them. We also went to the Barcelona zoo, Maremagnum, La Rambla, Mar Bella and the park.

Ammar Hussain (6)
Oldham Hulme Grammar School, Oldham

Dear Diary

Today, me and Monty the dog went to a magical forest to find a unicorn. I took a rucksack full of sweets and apples to feed it. I also took my magical map. We set off very early, it was 2am. It was very dark but the map glowed so I could see. When we got to the forest, it was still dark. I put the sweets and apples on a rock and I hid behind a bush to wait. I waited for a very, very long time, then I saw a unicorn eating my food. I put a headcollar on it and I took it home with us. I decided to call it Fluffy. It is now my pet.

Alessandro Guarino (6)
Oldham Hulme Grammar School, Oldham

Dear Diary

Today, I went to the park with my friend, he is called Jeremy. He was feeling sad and nobody could cheer him up. At the pond, we spotted a frog. The frog was a king. Jeremy said to the frog, "A witch turned me into this grumpy old man!"
The frog said, "Hold on to this shell, it will turn you back!"

Poppy Victoria Sykes (6)
Oldham Hulme Grammar School, Oldham

Dear Diary

One day, me and my best friend went to the funfair. First, we made slime. Next, we had some candyfloss. After that, we went on the big slide. Then we had a drink of orange juice and ate some doughnuts. After that, we had a rest and then we went and got some sweets. After that, we got a prize from the lucky dip and went on the bouncy castle. Then we won a teddy bear from one game. After, we had a chicken burger and we drank some water, then we went on the teacups. Finally, we went home and had a nice, big rest!

Khadijah Tulkubra Khan (6)
Rawdhatul Uloom Primary School, Burnley

Dear Diary

On Saturday, I went to the science festival with my mum. I saw a lizard, snail, snake and a tarantula. Did you know that snails have ten-thousand teeth and they breathe through the holes in their shell? I also learnt that tarantulas flick their hairs at their predators to make them itchy. Next, I saw germs on my hands under the UV light, yuck! I made a qualities bracelet which had colourful beads for tongue-rolling and other things. It was a fun day! I can't wait to go next year!

Salisha Vaghela (6)
Ribbleton Avenue Infant School, Preston

Dear Diary

Once I went to the zoo and all the zoo animals escaped. I was with my best friend, Thomas Brown. We were shocked. We ran into the park, we thought we were safe but... we weren't! The king of all animals, the lion, was lurking and circling the park with danger.

We crashed into the funfair where everyone was having a good time until the greediest, the naughtiest and the cheekiest animals came into the funfair.

They needed to be moved somewhere safer and further like Africa, so we moved them. A week into living there, we were tired of having to put on suncream every day. We also weren't allowed to dance. I don't know why?

Caleb Flood (7)

St Anne's Catholic Primary School, Leyland

Dear Diary

Yesterday, on the 13th July, I went on my first ever Brownie Guide camp. I had only just become a Brownie, so I just went for the day instead of sleeping over. My mum drove me to Guys Farm Activity Centre where I met up with the other Brownies and the leaders. I was very excited!

When I arrived, we went to the woods to build a fire and we toasted marshmallows and then we went to a glistening, sparkling lake. At the lake, we learnt to paddleboard and we swam in the lake too! After that, we played some games and then we headed back to the house to make fairy jars from old glass jars and the fairies left us some pixie dust. We then had pasta and garlic bread for tea and they had got me a birthday cake because it had been my birthday the week before! Yum! After tea, my mum arrived at 7pm to take me home.

On the way home, I told her how fantastic my day had been! I went to bed as soon as we got in because I was so tired from a fun-filled day. I had such a great time!

Alice Ciara Myerscough (7)

St Anne's Catholic Primary School, Leyland

Dear Diary

Today, I went to the funfair and I saw unicorns dancing around holding coloured balloons with amazing drawings. So, I decided to ask them what they were doing. When they saw me, they stepped back. The more I stepped forward, they stepped back. I thought they were scared, so I just went to get some candyfloss and that was delicious. I ran back to my mum and dad and said, "There are unicorns!"
"Nonsense!" they said. I had to make them believe so I showed them. When they got there, they were amazed at what they saw and they couldn't believe their eyes!

Amelia Cartmell (7)
St Anne's Catholic Primary School, Leyland

Dear Diary

You'll never guess what I did today! I had the best day ever because I went to Saturn and saw a golden space unicorn. I was surprised! I ate magical, golden rocks as well. The rings around me were stripes of orange and yellow. The stars glinted like the sun. I could see Planet Earth, much bigger than me. It was brighter than the stars I could see. Then I saw a gigantic space rocket zoom past me. It had bright red, yellow and orange fire at the bottom of the rocket. I got home by zooming back to Earth in my amazing jet pack. What a wonderful day!

Abigail Cleece (7)

St Anne's Catholic Primary School, Leyland

Dear Diary

The other day, I went to the seaside and I built a sandcastle. Next, I played in the sea and I saw a mermaid. There was a fairy above her. The mermaid's name was Amber and the fairy's name was Heather. The mermaid was trapped in a cage and the fairy was crying above her. A tear dropped down onto the mermaid's face. Then a unicorn flew from out of the cloud and flew down onto the cage and cracked the cage door. Then the mermaid wiped her tears away and flapped her tail to get out of the cage. Then she walked on her hands all the way back to the sea and there was a picnic waiting for her. We had some games and we danced and had a smoothie, it was amazing.

Willow Lea Layton (6)
St Anne's Primary School, Denton

Dear Diary

On Sunday, I went to the fair with my mum and it was exciting and I went on the big wheel and the roller coaster. Next, we ate some candyfloss. I loved it and I drank some cola. Then I played in the castle house and the queen house. Then my mum had a go on a big swing. Then I went on the sidekick and then had dinner. I had a hot dog and chips. It was yummy and then I went on the merry-go-round. I had lots of fun. I discovered everything, looked at all the rides and walked everywhere. Then, my mum had her lunch. She had pizza and fries and we had a milkshake. My mum had strawberry, I had chocolate, it was so good and I had so much fun!

Ruby Redfern (6)
St Anne's Primary School, Denton

Dear Diary

Last week, I went to the park in a car and I played some football there. There were pretty cafes and icy smoothies there. Then I played on the swings and the climbing frame was a bit scary as I climbed up it. On the swings, I got a tummy ache when it was going up and down. When I was walking I saw pretty birds in the sky and the bird was flying to his nest. I got up from the bench and did some bird watching and I loved it. The park was the best thing I had ever been to! I had the best day ever! At the park, there were lots of people and lots of birds. Then we drove home and I played with my toys and my brother. It was a lovely day!

Phoebe Alice Barnes (6)

St Anne's Primary School, Denton

Dear Diary

Last week, we went to Tatton Park. We got on the bus and I was so excited. When we got off, we saw a fairy godmother. She was so pretty. We visited Cinderella's mansion. We walked around and we looked around for Cinderella's mice. When we finished looking around the mansion, it was lunchtime. We had sandwiches and some of us had packed lunches. After lunch, we had a look in the queen's garden. We told stories, it was so fun. There were so many flowers and plants. We said goodbye to Cinderella. I had such a good time. Then we went back to school, it was the best time ever!

Olivia Rainey (6)
St Anne's Primary School, Denton

Dear Diary

One month ago, I went to the zoo with my family. We went to the orangutans. Next, I went to see a chameleon. Then I went to have my lunch. I had chips and a drink and we went to see a pelican and we saw another orangutan. He threw the ball at himself. We went to see the lemurs and they were cute. Then we went to the monkeys and they had moustaches and it was funny! We saw a seal and we saw a lion and a tiger. We saw three wolves and a gorilla. We saw another mummy monkey and a tiger, a snake, a koala and a panda and a giraffe and an elephant.

Kobe Kayes (6)
St Anne's Primary School, Denton

Dear Diary

Last week, we went to Tatton Park and we went on the coach. When we got off the coach, we saw a fairy godmother and the fairy godmother showed us the house. When we went into the house, the fairy godmother showed us all the rooms because she thought they were nice. We had a picture on the steps and then we did some of Cinderella's chores. We had lunch and, after lunch, we went into the forest to read some books. We went to the garden shop and we saw some of Cinderella's favourite flowers. When we got on the coach, I had a drink.

Isabelle Louise Connor (6)
St Anne's Primary School, Denton

Dear Diary

Last week, we went to Tatton Park and we went on a bus. When we got there, we saw a fairy godmother and looked around. Then we had lunch. I had a sandwich and an apple for lunch. Then we went into the garden. When we went into the garden, we read stories. The story was the Three Pigs and the Gingerbread Man. We read it with Cinderella. My favourite part was when the wolf blew the pig's house down and the gingerbread man ran away. Then I went back on the bus. I had so much fun looking around with Cinderella and the fairy godmother.

Lilah Mae Barratt (6)
St Anne's Primary School, Denton

Dear Diary

I went to the zoo last week and I saw lots of animals. First, we went to the tiger. Next, we went to see the birds and they sang. Then we went to the crocodiles and they had scales. After the crocodiles, we had lunch. After, we went to the meerkats and they were so cute. Then we went to the butterflies and one landed on me! Then we went to the giraffes and they had a long neck. After that, we went to the elephants, they were grey and they also had big, curly trunks. It sprayed me with water and the baby too!

Charlotte Delaney (6)
St Anne's Primary School, Denton

Dear Diary

The other day, we travelled to a park that was interesting. We talked to the toilets and walked to the mansion. We really enjoyed it and took a photo on the steps. Then we went into the forest and we did a story. That was in the garden! I was so excited! In the garden, there was a lawnmower that shortened the grass by itself. Then we walked to the toilets and back to the coach. Then we were back at school for a little bit. Me and my class had a really fun and interesting time. Have you been to Tatton Park?

Freddie Millington (5)
St Anne's Primary School, Denton

Dear Diary

The other day, we travelled to Tatton Park on a bus. When we got there, we saw a fairy godmother and it was Cinderella's fairy godmother. We walked with Cinderella's fairy godmother to the building and had a little story about Cinderella and when we said the magic words, which were, "Bibbity-bobbity-boo!" Cinderella was there! Then Cinderella came down the stairs and then she sat down on the chair. We loved it!

Georgia Ward (6)

St Anne's Primary School, Denton

Dear Diary

Last week, we went to Tatton Park. We went on a bus and I was excited. When we got off the bus, the fairy godmother was waiting for us and she was pretty. She looked around and we went behind a tree and the fairy godmother told us a story about the Three Pigs and the Gingerbread Man and Little Red Riding Hood. It was amazing and I loved it! We went back on the bus and we went back to school and went home. All of us enjoyed it.

Abbie Carney (6)
St Anne's Primary School, Denton

Dear Diary

Last week, we went to Tatton Park and when we got there, I was very excited. When we got there, we saw the fairy godmother and the fairy godmother took us to the mansion. In the mansion, the fairy godmother told us a story. When the story finished, Cinderella came down. Cinderella gave us some magic sand and we got back on the coach. It was very fun! Do you know what Tatton Park is like?

Ethan Healey (6)
St Anne's Primary School, Denton

Dear Diary

I went to horse-riding one day and I loved it because it was very good. After that, I went back home and I watched TV. Then I played out with my friends. After that, I did some art and it was very good but my friend did one too and I loved it. But, I loved mine the best. Then I went shopping and I loved it! So, we wanted to look at everything. I love shopping! I loved that day!

Lacey-Rae Cassidy (6)

St Anne's Primary School, Denton

Dear Diary

We went to Tatton Park. We got there by coach. I went with my friends. Our teacher told us to go to the other places we had to go. I went with Cinderella out on the grass. We went to have a dance. We went to the garden. We went to the bench and we did a story. We went back to school again and then we got ready for home time and we went home, it was fun!

Chloe McFarland (6)
St Anne's Primary School, Denton

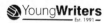

Dear Diary

The other day, I went to the zoo with my family. The first animal was the crocodile and I was very scared when I got to it. They let me feed it. The second animals were the penguins and they were so cute. The third animal was a monkey, he was very good at jumping. After that, we had lunch. That was the most amazing day ever! Then we went home.

Ella Macfarlane (6)
St Anne's Primary School, Denton

Dear Diary

Last week, I went to watch Detective Pikachu and the Secret Life of Pets 2 with my mummy and sisters. After that, we went to my friends and played out. After, I went to my cousins and played with them. After that, I went to the park near my house. After that, I went to the zoo. Then I went to my house and went to play!

Chloe Lewis (6)
St Anne's Primary School, Denton

Dear Diary

Last week, we went to Tatton Park. When we got there, we saw a fairy godmother and she led us in the mansion. Then we had lunch. After lunch, we went to the garden. In the garden, we had a story. After the story, we had a walk in the forest. We had another story and we saw a castle. In the castle was Snow White.

Max Thewlis (6)
St Anne's Primary School, Denton

Dear Diary

I went on the bus to Tatton Park and I saw a fairy. I went to the mansion and I saw Cinderella and we told tales. We visited all around the mansion. Then we had dinner. After we had dinner, we went to the garden and read the Three Little Pigs and Red Riding Hood and then we walked back to the bus!

Isabelle Chambers (6)

St Anne's Primary School, Denton

Dear Diary

Last week, we went to Tatton Park and went on the coach. When we got off the coach, we saw a fairy. Then we started walking with her. We went to have lunch in a cafe because it was dinner time and after dinner time, we went to the castle and we looked at all the different rooms.

Darcie Royle (6)
St Anne's Primary School, Denton

Dear Diary

I went to the zoo and the first animal was a tiger. Then I went to see a lion, they were scary. After that, I had my lunch and I had chicken, chips and beans. Then I went to the reptile house and I went to see a snake and a lizard.

Dominic Cocca (6)
St Anne's Primary School, Denton

Dear Diary

On holiday I went to Hydro Park, I had lots of fun. When we got to the wave pool, me and my friend Grace stayed in the same part, but my sister Grace went underneath the water because the waves were huge!

Freya Rose Marland (6)
St Anne's Primary School, Denton

Dear Diary

On Sunday, we went to the zoo. I saw an elephant and penguins. They were funny! They dove, they caught fish, they did everything! It was fun.

Lexie Cooper (5)
St Anne's Primary School, Denton

Dear Diary

Yesterday, I went on a school trip to the Sea Life Centre in Blackpool. First, I went on a coach to get there. Then I got a photo taken. Next, I explored inside. I saw a shark swimming inside the pool. When I had my lunch, I went on the beach. I built a sandcastle. I like the seahorse the most in the Sea Life Centre and, on the beach, I liked building a sandcastle. On the way home, I went back on the coach and I sat next to my friend, Carolina. I enjoyed it at the Sea Life Centre and I would like to go there again. I can still see the seahorses swimming in my imagination, I liked it so much.

Jessica Rose Gibson (6)
St Gabriel's CE Primary School, Middleton

Dear Diary

Yesterday, I went to the Sea Life Centre. First, we got our photo taken. Then I touched a starfish in the rock pool! Next, we saw a massive stingray. Then we saw an eel that looked like a rock. After that, we saw Matilda the eel, she looked mean! After dinner, we went to the beach and I played with my friends, it was fun! Then we went on the coach back to school and we had a great surprise. It was Blackpool rock!

Joshua Kian Swatkins (6)

St Gabriel's CE Primary School, Middleton

Dear Diary

Yesterday, I went to Blackpool Sea Life Centre. We went there by a white coach. First, we had our photo taken, then we explored. My best bit was the seahorses because they were so beautiful. Then, we had lunch. After lunch, we went to the beach, it was very, very fun. It was my first time. I was so excited at Blackpool Sea Life Centre. My best thing in Blackpool was the tower! I would go there again.

Carolina Mazur (6)
St Gabriel's CE Primary School, Middleton

Dear Diary

Yesterday, we went on a school trip to the Sea Life Centre. We explored. First, I touched a starfish. Then I saw a mermaid. After that, I saw a stingray. Then we had dinner. After dinner, we went to the beach. Then I dug for shells and treasure. After the beach, we went on the white coach and I sat next to Skye. Then we had a surprise, it was sweets! The Sea Life Centre was so much fun!

Aleeyah Jade Susan Samuels (6)
St Gabriel's CE Primary School, Middleton

Dear Diary

Yesterday, I went on a school trip to Blackpool Sea Life Centre. We got on a big, white coach. When we got there, we took off our coats. First, we had our photo taken. Then, we explored. We went to see the rock pool and we touched a spiky starfish. My favourite thing to do was taking the photos. After lunch, we went on the beach and I built a sandcastle and I would go again!

Ruby Lee Gibson (6)
St Gabriel's CE Primary School, Middleton

Dear Diary

Yesterday, I went to Blackpool Sea Life Centre. First, I got on a big, white coach, I sat next to my friend, Jess. It was a very, very long way there. When we got there, I had my photo taken, then we touched the sea creatures in the rock pool. That was my favourite part. After lunch, we went to the beach. I played in the sand. I really like it and I would like to go again!

Grace Turner (5)
St Gabriel's CE Primary School, Middleton

Dear Diary

Yesterday, it was our school trip. I went on a big, white coach to Blackpool Sea Life Centre. First, I went to the rockpool, I saw starfish. Did you know that a starfish has an eye on each leg? Next, I saw a clownfish and a jellyfish. Then I saw water coming down. After that, I went to the beach and I played with Isaac. Then I went back to the coach. I had so much fun!

Towasin Jimoh (6)
St Gabriel's CE Primary School, Middleton

Dear Diary

Yesterday, we all went on a school trip. We went to Blackpool Sea Life Centre. We got there on a big, white coach. First, we got our picture taken. Then we explored. My favourite thing was touching the sea creatures. The starfish felt spiky. We had a little snack, then we explored again and had lunch. After lunch, we went to the beach. It was lovely!

Aroush Asaf (6)
St Gabriel's CE Primary School, Middleton

Dear Diary

Our school trip to Blackpool was the Sea Life Centre. First, we went to the rock pool. I saw some crabs and I was not scared to touch the crab and the starfish. Then we saw a seahorse and a clownfish and a Dory fish. I loved the seahorse. After dinner, we went to the beach. I made a sandcastle of Blackpool Tower. We had a fabulous day! I love it!

Amelia-Jaye Josephine Jones-Horton (6)

St Gabriel's CE Primary School, Middleton

Dear Diary

Yesterday, I went to Blackpool Sea Life Centre. I went on a big, white coach. I sat next to my friend, Oliver. It took a really long time. I went to the rock pool. I saw a big shark! After the Sea Life Centre, I went to the beach. On the beach, I played with Robin and Tommy. I had a really fun time.

Zac H (6)
St Gabriel's CE Primary School, Middleton

Dear Diary

The other day, we went on a trip to the Isle of Wight. When I got to my granny's, I went to sleep, then I went to my gran's wedding. Then, I did crazy golf! Then we went to the beach, then we went home. I loved it very much at the beach. I was digging for rocks and shells.

Harry Carl Turner (6)
St Gabriel's CE Primary School, Middleton

Dear Diary

We went on a school trip to the Sea Life Centre. First, we went to the rock pool. I touched the starfish. I saw a big jellyfish. Next, we saw Matilda. She was a green eel. I loved the seahorse. After dinner, we went to the beach. I played in the sand. I had a brilliant time!

Jacob Harvey-Tait (6)
St Gabriel's CE Primary School, Middleton

Dear Diary

Yesterday, I went to the Sea Life Centre. First, we had a photograph. Then we went to the rock pool. I touched a starfish. Then we saw a shark. After that, I had my lunch. Next, we went to the beach. I played with the ball. On the way back, I sat next to my friend Ruby.

Elouise Blore (6)
St Gabriel's CE Primary School, Middleton

Dear Diary

Today, we went to the Sea Life Centre. I saw a starfish, I touched it in the rock pool and I touched a crab. I saw Matilda, she looked like a long, green snake. After dinner, we went to the beach. I dug a big hole in the sand and I saw Blackpool Tower. I loved our trip!

Millie Brooke Humphries (6)
St Gabriel's CE Primary School, Middleton

Dear Diary

Yesterday, we went on a big, white coach and we went to the Sea Life Centre in Blackpool. When we got there, we went to the rock pool. I touched a starfish, it was spiky. After lunch, we all went to the beach and played on the beach. I would go again!

Lily-Rose Davies (6)
St Gabriel's CE Primary School, Middleton

Dear Diary

The other day, we went to the Sea Life Centre. First, we went to the rock pools. I touched the grey starfish, it felt bumpy. Then we saw a sea snake. After, we went to play on the beach. I collected seashells. I had a great day on the trip.

Isaac Harvey-Tait (6)
St Gabriel's CE Primary School, Middleton

Dear Diary

Yesterday, I went to the Sea Life Centre in Blackpool and we went on a big, white coach and it took a really long time to get there. When we got there, we saw a shark. Sharks can eat us! After lunch, we went to the beach and I liked it.

Noah-Kie Hudson (6)
St Gabriel's CE Primary School, Middleton

Dear Diary

Yesterday, I went to the Sea Life Cente. I was excited and I was happy and I loved the beach. I played on the beach, I was making a sandcastle. I loved my keyring. After that, I went to the shark tunnel. I want to go again!

Kenley Smith (5)
St Gabriel's CE Primary School, Middleton

Dear Diary

Today, I went to the zoo. I went with Mum, Dad and Phoebe. I went to eat lunch and I ate yummy pizza. Then I went to see the jaguar. Then I went to see the giraffes, they were very spotty. After that, I went to see the lizard, he was camouflaged! Then I went to see the cute panda. Afterwards, I went to see the Komodo dragon, he was very ferocious. Then I went to see the ginormous elephant. I went to see eight little mice. Later, I went to see the black and white zebra. Then I went to see the salamanders. After a very busy day, I went home.

Lucas James Burgess (6)
The Deans Primary School, Swinton

Dear Diary

Today, I went to gymnastics with my friendly monster. We had a lot of fun. I taught my monster a handstand, then we had a drink. After that, we ate pasta and the friendly monster made a lot of mess. Then we did some more gymnastics! We had a very fun time at gymnastics. Then we did cartwheels and roly polys. Then we left gymnastics and went to the cinema. We watched the Lion King. We got popcorn and a big drink. It was a very sad and happy story. We had a good time and we snuggled in bed.

Mia King (6)
The Deans Primary School, Swinton

Dear Diary

Today, I went to the park with my best friend and we played on the swings. We ate some delicious, yummy pizza with strawberry milkshakes. I also went with my mum, dad, sister and baby brother. It was a warm, sunny, bright day. Then we were hungry again and we saw an ice cream van. We licked the ice cream and we had a brilliant day. We were tired so we had a break. After having a break, we went on the see-saw, then we went back home.

Khadija Senussi (6)

The Deans Primary School, Swinton

Dear Diary

Yesterday, I went to the zoo and I went with my sister, my mum and my dad. First, we bought the tickets. Then, we walked inside. We saw the cheeky monkeys. I got to hold a monkey! Then, I went to see the tigers. When we saw the tigers, it was on a hill but they were sleeping. I went to the cafe and I ate a delicious cheese pizza. After that, my mum bought a red, yummy milkshake.

Isabella Ho (6)
The Deans Primary School, Swinton

Dear Diary

Yesterday, I went to Butlins. I had a brilliant time. I went with my nana, sister and mummy. I went to the water park. It was a bright, sunny day. Then I went to the disco, it was colourful and bright. I loved the dots, I tried to catch the dots with my sister. I ate a delicious barbecue. We went home, then we played outside.

Alivia Wheeldon (6)
The Deans Primary School, Swinton

Dear Diary

Yesterday, I went to the funfair and I had a brilliant time. I went with my fabulous mum and my charming dad. I saw an obstacle course. I couldn't manage the first part so my mum helped me. First, I went on the Ferris wheel with my mummy, it was fun. After, we went to the cafe and I had a strawberry milkshake.

Jaxon Ronnie Openshaw (6)
The Deans Primary School, Swinton

Dear Diary

Yesterday, I went to the zoo. First, I saw the penguins, then I saw baby tigers and then I saw the giraffes. Then I saw baby elephants. After that, I saw some baby monkeys. The sun was bright! I ate some pizza with a vanilla milkshake, it was delicious food. I saw baby lions and we had great fun!

Matilde Pinto (6)

The Deans Primary School, Swinton

Dear Diary

Yesterday, I went to the amazing park. I had a brilliant time. I went with my mum and best friend. It was a sunny day and we ate burgers and chips. I went on the slide, it was a silver slide. We had watermelon and grapes. We went on the swing and we went on the monkey bars, then we went home.

Scarlett Faulkner (6)
The Deans Primary School, Swinton

Dear Diary

Today, I played football and I won some medals. After that, I ate some yummy pizza and drank Sprite. I found a shiny diamond in the middle of the pitch and found a secret door under it, there were lions in it. Then we went home. At home, we had to brush our teeth, then we went to bed.

Anthony White (6)

The Deans Primary School, Swinton

Dear Diary

I went to the park with my mum and my sister and my baby. We played on the slide and, after, we went on the monkey bars. Then we had some ham sandwiches and cucumber and watermelon. Then I played on the swing. Then me and my sister went on the roundabout and, finally, we went home.

Mollie Griffin (5)
The Deans Primary School, Swinton

Dear Diary

The other week, I went to Wales. I went with Dad, Mum, my brother and my cousin. Then we went to the caravan. We had food and we had watermelon, grapes and water. Then we went to the disco. After that, we went back to the caravan.

Poppy Grace Atkinson (6)
The Deans Primary School, Swinton

150

Dear Diary

Today, I went to the beach and I went into the water. I went with my mum and dad. I ate a scrumptious, cheesy, yummy pizza. I also drank some yummy apple juice. I had ice cream with a cherry on top, it was chocolate flavoured.

Andrei Toma Lupu (6)
The Deans Primary School, Swinton

Dear Diary

Yesterday, I went to space. I saw aliens and I saw the other planets. The planets were gigantic and sparkly. I ate a delicious hamburger and a milkshake. Finally, I went home with some candyfloss.

Joseph Green (6)

The Deans Primary School, Swinton

Dear Diary

Yesterday, I went to the park. First, we went on the swings. Next, we went on the roundabout. Then I had a cheese sandwich. Then I had some pasta and it was delicious. Then we travelled back home.

Emma Gunn-Russell (6)
The Deans Primary School, Swinton

Dear Diary

I went to a football ground and I went to watch Manchester United against Chelsea. I went with my dad. When it was half-time, I had a scrumptious sandwich. It was a penalty shootout. Chelsea won!

Harry Kirby (6)

The Deans Primary School, Swinton

Dear Diary

Yesterday, I went to the park. I went on the swings. After, I went on the slide. After, I went to the cafe with Daddy and Mummy. I ate some food and I drank a strawberry milkshake.

Darcie Savannah Collins (5)

The Deans Primary School, Swinton

Dear Diary

Yesterday, we went to the zoo with Mum and Dad and we saw a red fox. We also saw a big, tall giraffe. Then we saw a blue, light fish. After that, we saw a big, gigantic elephant.

Evan Millward (6)

The Deans Primary School, Swinton

Dear Diary

Yesterday, I went to McDonald's. I went with my friend's dad. I ate a cheesy burger and a chocolate milkshake. Then I went home.

Giuseppe Ferlito (6)

The Deans Primary School, Swinton

Dear Diary

The other day, my friend, the alien, flew in his spaceship and he landed in my garden. I went in his spaceship and we went to the planet Mars. We went to the cafe in space and had a fabulous day. We both had some chips and fish, then we went to the dark side of the moon. We met another alien, he wasn't nice. We ran back to the rocket and blasted off onto Planet Cheese where there was another cafe. There was a menu, it had a lot of food and we had more fish and chips. The fish and chips tasted salty and tasty. Then we had a campfire. The campfire was hot. Then we had a snack and a feast with all of our friends. Everyone had a good time, then I had to go. I jumped into the rocket and I flew my rocket and blasted back home.

Edward Hill (6)
Weeton Primary School, Weeton

Dear Diary

I had the best, most fabulous day ever. Well, I went outside and I saw a space rocket and there was a three-eyed alien in it. I was stressed. I had never seen an alien before. It was weird to meet an alien. I felt weird. We went to the hot desert, it was very bright. I was out of breath so we had a rest. When it was time to go, I was jolly. But, as we were just leaving, we found a precious diamond. It looked colourful. We took it with us and we said goodbye and I hope I see the alien again. With a flash, she was gone. I was very sad but I remembered the fun I had.

Poppy Reid (6)
Weeton Primary School, Weeton

Dear Diary

In the summer, I went to Wales. I went in a caravan, it was hot. When I went in it, I was very hot. After that, I played Guess Who? I won! Then I fed sheep, they were very cute. Then I watched a movie called the Jungle Book. I had a good time in Wales. I fed chickens and then we went to the shop to get lunch which was pasta. Then I played in my room.

Poppie Mai Malone (6)
Weeton Primary School, Weeton

Dear Diary

I have had the coolest day ever. I have been to space! I met a three-eyed alien, it was so fun. I went to the moon. I loved it. I played tag, it was amazing. I wished it would never end. Then we got to the moon. There were ugly, scary, massive aliens and jolly aliens. There were tiny, massive, jolly, ugly, sharp, bright and fast aliens!

Phoebe Greener (5)
Weeton Primary School, Weeton

Dear Diary

Yesterday, I went to my grandpa's caravan. I was excited because we went to the slots and I won lots of Haribo. Then we went back and I brushed my teeth. Then I saw a mouse in my dream but then it was morning and we could go to the slots or shopping.

Elliot Jack Bostock (6)
Weeton Primary School, Weeton

Dear Diary

Today, I went to the beach. I made a sandcastle and then I went in the waves. I ate some sand and then I swam along the waves. I like the beach. I played on the swings, then I went to the funfair. Then I went back to the beach and then I went home.

Bai Ebrahim Saine (6)
Weeton Primary School, Weeton

Dear Diary

I had an amazing day. I wished it would never end. I went to the beach. But, our car broke and we had to walk to the beach. At the beach, I played in the sea. We packed up and went home on time. On the way, I had a little nap.

Ebony Murphy (6)
Weeton Primary School, Weeton

Dear Diary

I have had a cool day! Yesterday, I went to the South Pole. I had my coat because it was cold! I met a polar bear and the polar bear was very nice and the polar bear was white.

Keevagh Quaggan (6)
Weeton Primary School, Weeton

Dear Diary

The other day, I went to space with an alien and we went to the zoo. The alien looked scary but it was nice. We saw a chimpanzee on a trampoline, it was very fun!

Tommy James Edkins (6)
Weeton Primary School, Weeton

Dear Diary

One day, I woke up. I brushed my stinky, smelly teeth. Next, I had breakfast, then in my window, I saw a slimy, green monster. The monster said, "I am going to space, can you go with me?"
"But, I don't have a spaceship!"
"I do!"
"Okay." So I got ready. Next, we went into space and we saw the moon and the sun and even the Earth. The sun was hot, so we put our sunglasses on. We went to the moon, we saw a shop and the shop was called the Ice Cream Shop. It was there because the sun was hot. Next, we fell asleep. After, we played video games!

Safwan Noor Chowdhury (6)
Westwood Prep School, Oldham

Dear Diary

Today, a huge, gigantic monster came to the town. I decided to put my superhero suit on! The monster was scary and evil, it had a pot with a spoon, it was poisonous. I bravely said, "You're not getting away with this!" "How are you going to destroy me?" I got his pot and put it on him and he died.

Muhammed Saleem (6)
Westwood Prep School, Oldham

Young Writers Information

We hope you have enjoyed reading this book – and that you will continue to in the coming years.

If you're a young writer who enjoys reading and creative writing, or the parent of an enthusiastic poet or story writer, do visit our website **www.youngwriters.co.uk**. Here you will find free competitions, workshops and games, as well as recommended reads, a poetry glossary and our blog. There's lots to keep budding writers motivated to write!

If you would like to order further copies of this book, or any of our other titles, then please give us a call or order via your online account.

Young Writers
Remus House
Coltsfoot Drive
Peterborough
PE2 9BF
(01733) 890066
info@youngwriters.co.uk

Join in the conversation!
Tips, news, giveaways and much more!

 YoungWritersUK    @YoungWritersCW